Christmas 2021

Dear Elliott,

May all your fishing adventures be filled with fun!

Love
Aunt Linda ♡

Brownie & Bo at the Big Wood Diner

WRITTEN BY Lynn W. Peters   ILLUSTRATED BY Zack D. Brown

Mandala Media
Book Publishing Division

313 N. Main St. Hailey, Idaho

BROWNIE & BO AT THE BIG WOOD DINER
© LYNN W. PETERS, 2016

Published by Mandala Media, LLC
313 North Main Street
Hailey, Idaho 83333, USA

Book design by Mandala Media, a team of artists and editors
who collaborate on design and printed book projects.

To contact the author, please email brownieandbo@gmail.com.

Library of Congress Cataloging-in-Publication data is available on request.
ISBN: 978-0-9834470-6-1
First Edition 2016
Printed in the USA

Dedicated

to my husband Tim for his enduring love
through all of our years and on so many rivers

and

to Tripp, Kent, Markley and Grady, the young fisher-people in our family,
for the joy that they bring to our lives. Along with catching fish,
I hope that they have caught an appreciation
for the wonders of the wilderness.

And with sincere thanks to

Zack for giving color and life to Brownie and Bo's story,

and

Laurie, Kate and Adam, whose hard work and passion for this project,
from start to finish, made this book possible.

"Hey there, Brownie, what do you say?
It really is a blue bird day.

What a great day for swimming and hanging out
here in the Big Wood River," said Bo, a rainbow trout.

"We have majestic mountains, reaching high,
that almost touch the bright blue sky.

Here, clear rivers bubble and flow.
How lucky we are," said Brownie to Bo.

"But wait, there's more to tell of this wandering river.
I've heard tales," said Bo, "to make your scales quiver.

Some of these fisher-people are really quite sly.
They can trick you into falling for a line and fake fly.

Others plop flies all over that you really must dodge.
They need to go to a casting clinic up at Sun Valley Lodge."

"It's certainly no fun to find a sharp hook in your meal
but how can you know," Brownie asked, "if it's attached to a reel?"

"Save your tales of adventure for a little bit, Bo.
I'm getting mighty hungry, that really is so.

I could munch on some baetis or any tasty mayfly,
whatever the river serves up for a real hungry guy."

"Just be careful," said Bo, "and use both your eyes.
You don't want to be tricked by any feathery flies."

"Did I ever tell you about my friend Bullwinkle up at Pettit Lake?"
Bo shivered as he recalled when Winkle fell for a fake.

"He chomped down on a fake and was hooked beyond any doubt,
but was saved when a sign told that fisherman: *Release All Bull Trout*.

So Winkle went back in that lake, quick as a flash,
where he still swims now, not making a splash."

10

"Go ahead," said Brownie, "tell me some more.
Maybe I'll forget how hungry I was before."

29

"Well, my old Uncle Rainy is from my mother's side of the clan.
He tells quite a story about his encounter with a man.

He lives in Silver Creek," said Bo, "down Picabo way,
where the trout are both whoppers and smart, so they say."

"Now Uncle Rainy," said Bo,
"is as elusive as a trout can get,
but somehow, someway,
he ended up in a net!"

"Rainy claimed the experience wasn't really all bad
and the guy who caught him was a right gentle lad.

He had the hook out of Rainy's lip quick as could be,
and put him back in Silver Creek before you could count to three.

The legend did grow, at least so they say,
and Uncle Rainy was the talk of the town that day.

Yet each time that fisherman told his tall tale,
the longer Uncle Rainy became from tip to tail."

"That's a great story," said Brownie to Bo,
"but I have to eat something soon, that much I know.

People are lucky, they just walk into a store,
look up on the shelves and find food galore.

But there aren't any grocery stores for us fish,
nor waiters to serve us our favorite dish.

We must wait until the moment is just right,
and then we swim up and take a great big bite."

Both Brownie and Bo then decided to rise
and feast on some delicious mayflies.

Brownie gobbled up a real one, enjoying his luck,
but Bo made an error and soon he was stuck.

He felt something tug and fought with all his might,
but was steadily being pulled up into the light.

"Look, Dad, look," Bo heard someone shout.
"I just caught a huge rainbow trout!"

Bo was out of the water for a quick photo op,
then back in the Big Wood, he went with a plop.

WOOD ⠀⠀⠀⠀⠀⠀⠀⠀⠀ RIVER

What did he say to Brownie about his adventure in air?
What did he think about his time up there?

"I'm glad the Big Wood here is catch and release.
I didn't want to end my days in a fry pan of grease!"

Fun Facts About
How They Live

Bull Trout

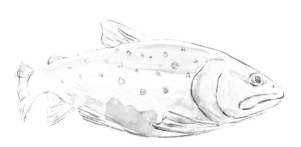

Bullwinkle is a bull trout. They were once common in the Pacific Northwest, but now they are threatened and protected by the Endangered Species Act. It is illegal to harvest bull trout, and there are signs helping fishermen identify them so they can release them back into the river.

Rainbow Trout

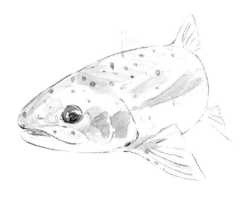

Bo and Uncle Rainy are rainbow trout. They are native to the rivers and lakes of North America west of the Rocky Mountains. Since fisherman love to fish for them, they have been introduced to rivers and streams all over the world.

Brown Trout

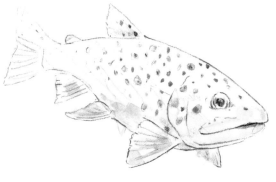

Brownie is a brown trout. They are native to Europe but were introduced into North America in the late 1800s.

A group of trout is called a Hover.

Brownie and Bo
and Where They Go

Water Quality

Many trout, especially rainbows and bull trout, are indicators of water quality because they can only live in clear, clean water. They prefer cool streams with gravel bottoms and natural cover. Most trout live for 4 to 6 years in the wild.

Spawning

Spawning is when a female trout digs a depression in a stream bed (which is called a redd) and then lays thousands of eggs. For every 1000 eggs laid, about 100 hatch (alevin), 10 make it to juvenile stage (fry) and only one becomes a reproducing adult trout.

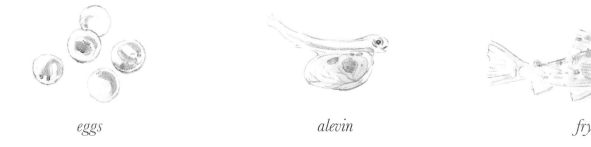

eggs   *alevin*   *fry*

To go fishing you need...

a rod

a fly

a reel

and a net

Flies

Flies that fishermen use should look like the insects that are hatching, since those are what the fish in that river will be eating. A fly fisherman always tries to **match the hatch**. Look at the mayfly (*Ephemeroptera*) samples below. Can you tell which one is the real fly and which one is the fisherman's fake fly?

Pale Morning Dun	Trico	Blue Winged Olive (Baetis)
Ephemerellidae	*Leptohyphidae*	*Baetidae*

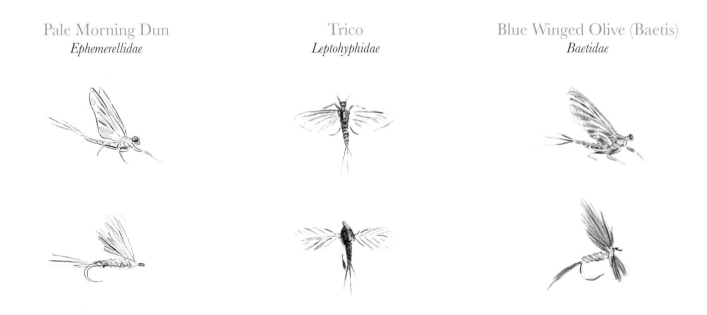

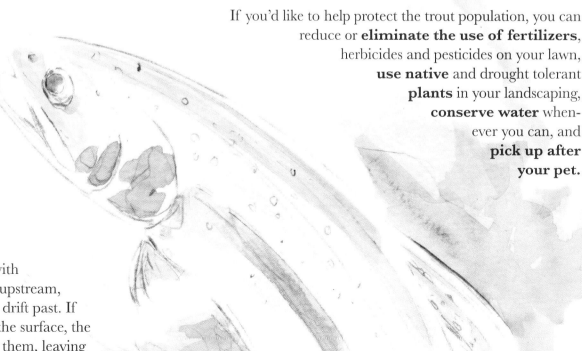

Here's where you can find Brownie & Bo

This story is based in the mountains of **Idaho**, a place of cool, clear waters where trout thrive.

The **Big Wood River** flows for 137 miles through the mountains of central Idaho near the town of Ketchum. It has a large number of rainbow trout and a good number of brown trout.

Silver Creek, near the small town of Picabo, Idaho (south of Ketchum in the Wood River Valley), is a spring-fed tributary of the Little Wood River. It is a world-renowned fly-fishing preserve. And fishermen travel from all over the earth just to fish its waters, enjoy the scenery and for a chance to catch a huge brown or rainbow trout.

Pettit Lake is a large alpine lake in the Sawtooth Valley south of Stanley, Idaho.

Here's how you can help protect Brownie & Bo

Catch and Release means that after a fish is caught, it is gently unhooked and quickly returned to the water so it can live to grow and have babies and be caught another day. Using **barbless hooks** helps minimize any damage to fish that you catch and release.

Trout Unlimited is a trout and salmon conservation organization dedicated to the conservation, protection and restoration of North America's cold water fisheries.

If you'd like to help protect the trout population, you can reduce or **eliminate the use of fertilizers**, herbicides and pesticides on your lawn, **use native** and drought tolerant **plants** in your landscaping, **conserve water** whenever you can, and **pick up after your pet.**

"Holding"

Trout will **"hold"** with their noses pointing upstream, watching for food to drift past. If there are insects on the surface, the fish will "rise" to eat them, leaving telltale rings on the water.

Pettit Lake

The End

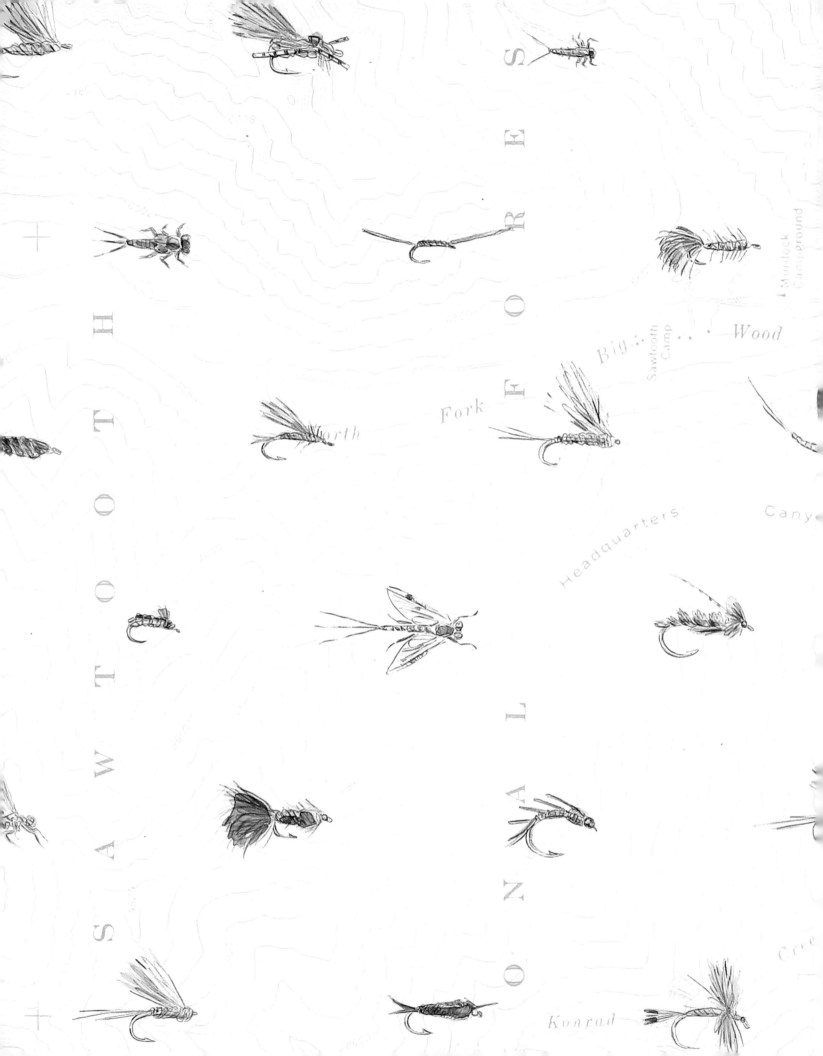